Y0-AQV-486

TWO HARBORS
TRAVELING LIBRARY

TWO HARBORS
TRAVELING LIBRARY

SQUARE AS A HOUSE

by
KARLA KUSKIN

Harper & Brothers

Publishers N. Y.

Books by KARLA KUSKIN

ROAR AND MORE

JAMES AND THE RAIN

IN THE MIDDLE OF THE TREES

THE ANIMALS AND THE ARK

JUST LIKE EVERYONE ELSE

WHICH HORSE IS WILLIAM?

SQUARE AS A HOUSE

SQUARE AS A HOUSE
Copyright © 1960 by Karla Kuskin
Printed in the United States of America
All rights in this book are reserved.
Library of Congress catalog card number: 60-5783

FOR URSULA

What would you choose
If you were free
To be anything fat
That you wanted to be?
Anything thin or long or tall,

Anything red, blue, black, at all;
A bird on the wing
Or a fish on the fin?
If you're ready to choose
It is time to begin.

If you could be square
Would you be a box
Containing a cake
Or a house
Or blocks
With painted letters
From A to Z?
Who would you
Which would you
What would you be?

If you could be soft
Would you be the snow
Or twenty-five pillows
Or breezes that blow
The blossoms that fall from
The sassafras tree?
Who would you
Which would you
What would you be?

If you could be loud
Would you be the sound
Of thunder at night
Or the howl of a hound
As he bays at the moon
Or the pound of the sea?
Who would you
Which would you
What would you be?

If you could be red
Would you be a car
That races the wind
Or jam in a jar
Or an acrobat's tights
With a hole in the knee?
Who would you
Which would you
What would you be?

If you could be small
Would you be a mouse
Or a mouse's child
Or a mouse's house
Or a mouse's house's
Front door key?
Who would you
Which would you
What would you be?

If you could be fat
Would you be a bear
Or a fat black cat
In a fat blue chair?
Would you be a ball
And bounce to me?
Who would you
Which would you
What would you be?

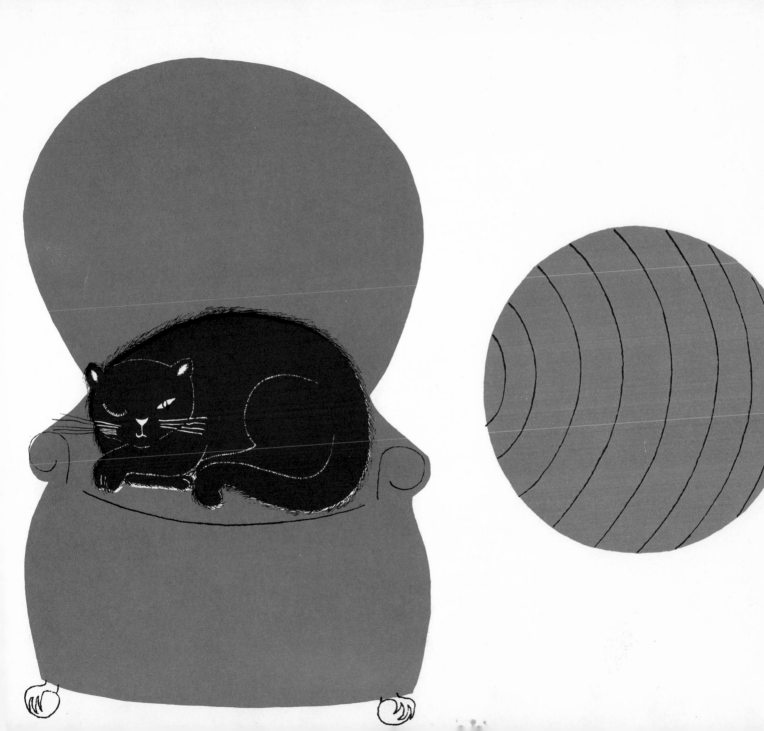

If you could be fierce
And roar with rage
Would you be a tiger
And tramp your cage?
Would you be a dragon
Or two or three?
Who would you
Which would you
What would you be?

If you could be dark
Would you be the night
Or a house on a hill
Where there wasn't a light
Or a witch watcher
Watching a witch with glee?
Who would you
Which would you
What would you be?

If you could be somebody
Holding a book
Who looked just exactly
The way that you look,
Who turned all these pages
And then said, "I'm through,"
Could you be
Should you be
Would you be you?